EX LIBRIS

*RICHARD A. BARD*

Give ye good-den,
Sweet gentlemen. *(Page 55)*

# More Silver Pennies

BY

## BLANCHE JENNINGS THOMPSON

HEAD OF THE ENGLISH DEPARTMENT, BENJAMIN FRANKLIN HIGH SCHOOL, ROCHESTER, NEW YORK

Illustrated by Pelagie Doane

NEW YORK

The Macmillan Company

1948

# TO MY GODCHILDREN

## TO THOSE WHO WANT MORE
## SILVER PENNIES

I<small>T IS</small> quite a long time ago that I gathered the
first silver pennies. Many have said that they
liked them, and many have asked for more. Silver
pennies are not so easy to find now, but I am sure
that I have some you will like. You will find old
friends among them and new ones that want to be
friends. The poems in Part One are for younger
readers, and those in Part Two are for you who
are older. Many, I hope, will grow with you.
The poems you cherish in youth will still be your
friends in age, for no matter how old you grow

> *You still need a silver penny*
> *To get into Fairyland.*

B<small>LANCHE</small> J<small>ENNINGS</small> T<small>HOMPSON</small>

# CONTENTS

## PART ONE

x

# PART TWO

# PART ONE

Och, hush ye then, och hush ye—
The night is dark an' wet.  (*Page 17*)

# EVERYBODY SAYS

*Nearly everyone can sympathize with the little girl in this poem, since most of us have had the same experience ourselves.*

EVERYBODY says
I look just like my mother.
Everybody says
I'm the image of Aunt Bee.
Everybody says
My nose is like my father's,
But *I* want to look like *me*.

DOROTHY ALDIS

1

## ABOUT BUTTONS

*Everyone has button trouble at one time or another.
Of course we ought to have our buttons sewed on
firmly; but when they come off, three cheers for the
man who invented safety pins!*

Every button has a door
    Which opens wide to let him in;
But when he rolls upon the floor,
Because he's tired of where he's been
And we can't find him any more,
    We use a pin.

DOROTHY ALDIS

## LITTLE BROTHER'S SECRET

*When children are very small and just learning about
this interesting world, they often have strange ideas
about things. Can you remember any queer ideas
that you used to have?*

When my birthday was coming
    Little Brother had a secret.

He kept it for days and days
And just hummed a little tune when I
    asked him.
But one night it rained,
And I woke up and heard him crying:
Then he told me.
"I planted two lumps of sugar in your
    garden
Because you love it so frightfully.
I thought there would be a whole sugar
    tree for your birthday.
And now it will be all melted."
Oh, the darling!

KATHARINE MANSFIELD

# WISHES

*In these days, when everybody seems to be trying to look like somebody else, it is well to remember that the most attractive people are those who look like themselves. If you could choose, how would you want to look?*

I WISH my eyes were big and blue,
　　And I had golden curls;
I wish my legs were fatter, too,
Like other little girls'!

I'd love a dimple in my chin;
　　I wish my mouth were small —
And, oh, the way my teeth fit in
I do not like at all!

But Daddy says he really thinks
　　That when I get my growth,
I'll look like mother. "Cheer up, Jinks!"
He says, and hugs us both.

How very splendid that would be!
　　I wonder if it's true —

For mother says that she can see
I'm daddy — through and through!

And they don't look alike one bit;
  It's queer as queer can be
That I can look like both and it
Just makes me look like me!

And when I wish my hair would curl
  And that my eyes were blue,
My mother says, "No, little girl —
For then you'd not be you!"

EDNA KINGSLEY WALLACE

5

# GROWING UP

*Growing up can be a very trying process, especially in a large family who are fond of teasing. We ought to be considerate enough not to tease in public anyway. Did you know that "bandy" means "bowlegged"?*

I'M GROWING very big and tall,
   Almost to mother's shoulder;
And though some things of course I like,
In getting to be older,


My legs and arms have grown so long
That father laughs and Bobby
Just grins and says, "Oh, gee, Pauline,
Your knees are awful knobby!"


And uncle calls me "Spindle-shanks"
And "Polly-doodle-dandy"
And says, "My child, be thankful that
Your lovely legs aren't bandy."

It's nice to reach high hooks and things,
If anybody pleases,
But I do wish my family
Weren't all such awful teases.

I don't know where to *put* myself
When mother tries to hold me;
I wish she knew some comfy way
To take me up and fold me.

Of course she's always letting down
My skirts and sleeves to hide me —
But, oh, I wish my bones would wait
Till I grow up inside me!

EDNA KINGSLEY WALLACE

7

# THE WAGON IN THE BARN

*This is an English poem, and the word "starn" is the way some of the country people in England say "stern." Since the stern of a boat is the back, you can guess where the scarecrow has his patch.*

THERE are mushrooms in the paddock,
    And walnuts on the trees,
And a hive in the corner
    To keep the honey-bees;
There's a hay-rick in the rick-yard,
    And another one of wheat,
And there are cooking apples,
    And other ones to eat.

There are berries on the bushes,
    The yellow ones and red,
There are starlings in the willows,
    And swallows in the shed;
There's a scarecrow in the garden,
    With a patch upon his starn,
But the thing that I like best is
    The wagon in the barn.

For in the rainy weather,
  We all climb up inside,
And we have a team of horses
  To take us for a ride;
And although they think we're playing
  In the barn because it rains,
We go riding in the wagon
  For miles along the lanes.

JOHN DRINKWATER

# IRISH

*Here is a lilting little poem that almost makes you dance a jig. Did you ever make a whistle of a willow twig or a hollow reed?*

MY FATHER and mother were Irish,
 And I am Irish, too;
I pipe you my bag of whistles,
And it is Irish, too.
I will sing with you in the morning,
And play with you at noon,
And dance with you in the evening
To a little Irish tune.
For my father and mother were Irish,
And I am Irish, too;
And here is my bag of whistles,
For it is Irish, too.

EDWARD J. O'BRIEN

10

# GENTLE NAME

*Names are very interesting. Sometimes they seem to fit people, and often they are all wrong. Did you ever look up the meaning of your own name? Some names have quite fascinating histories.*

M ARY is a gentle name
    Like the sound of silver bells,
Like a blue and quiet flame,
Like country brooks and ferny smells;
A friendly, wistful name and airy —
Mary.

SELMA ROBINSON

## GOLDENHAIR

*The name "Goldenhair" has a fairy sound. Some of the old tales use that name instead of "Goldilocks." Which do you like better? The Goldenhair in the poem was a real little girl.*

L EAN out of the window,
    Goldenhair;

I heard you singing
A merry air.

My book was closed;
I read no more,
Watching the fire dance
On the floor.

I have left my book,
I have left my room,
For I heard you singing
Through the gloom.

Singing and singing
A merry air,
Lean out of the window,
Goldenhair.

JAMES JOYCE

# CRADLE SONG

*Very few women in the great, teeming country of India have ever become known outside their own homes or villages, but Saroﾃini Naidu is an exception. She has done much to make the lot of Indian women easier, and in addition she writes beautiful poetry. This is a cradle song written for one of her own children. The neem is a big tree that grows in India.*

FROM groves of spice,
 O'er fields of rice,
Athwart the lotus-stream,
 I bring for you,
 Aglint with dew,
A little lovely dream.


 Sweet, shut your eyes,
 The wild fire-flies
Dance through the fairy *neem;*
 From the poppy-bole
 For you I stole
A little lovely dream.

Dear eyes, good night,
In golden light
The stars around you gleam;
On you I press
With soft caress
A little lovely dream.

SAROJINI NAIDU

14

# HUSHING SONG

*Fiona Macleod is the pen name used by a famous writer and scholar, William Sharp. He loved to discover and collect lovely, lost, old poems written by the Celts, who lived in Great Britain long, long ago. This poem is an ancient lullaby.*

EILY, Eily,
  My bonnie wee lass:
The winds blow,
  And the hours pass.


But never a wind
  Can do thee wrong,
Brown Birdeen, singing
  Thy bird-heart song.


And never an hour
  But has for thee
Blue of the heaven
  And green of the sea:

15

Blue for the hope of thee,
    Eily, Eily;
Green for the joy of thee,
    Eily, Eily.

Swing in thy nest, then,
    Here on my heart,
Birdeen, Birdeen,
    Here on my heart,
    Here on my heart!

FIONA MACLEOD

16

# Hush Song

*Here is another lullaby, this time in the Irish dialect.
All the mothers in the fishing villages want their boys
to be strong and hardy in order to follow the sea, but
there's always a fear in their hearts when the menfolk
are out on the deep.*

Och, hush ye then, och hush ye —
    There's herrin's in the bay,
An' you'll be the wee fisherman
Some day — some day.

Och, rest ye then, och rest ye —
    The herrin's do be small,
An' you're the boy when you'll be big
Will catch them all.

Och, hush ye then, och hush ye —
    The night is dark an' wet,
An' you too wee, och heart o' mine,
For fishin' yet.

Och, hush ye then, och hush ye —
    'Tis cowld upon the sea,

But this wee house is warm itself
For you an' me.

Och, sleep ye now, och sleep ye—
For sure a night will come
When you'll be wakin' on the sea,
An' me at home.

ELIZABETH SHANE

18

# FAIRIES

*If what Nurse says is really true, what chance do you*
*think that you will ever have of seeing a fairy?*

You can't see fairies unless you're good,
   That's what Nurse said to me.
They live in the smoke of the chimney,
   Or down in the roots of a tree;
They brush their wings on a tulip,
   Or hide behind a pea.

But you can't see fairies unless you're good,
   So they aren't much use to me.

MARCHETTE GAYLORD CHUTE

# I KEEP THREE WISHES READY

*Of course, if you should be so fortunate as to meet a*
*fairy, there's nothing like being prepared, as this*
*poem suggests.*

I KEEP three wishes ready,
   Lest I should chance to meet,

Any day a fairy
Coming down the street.

I'd hate to have to stammer,
Or have to think them out,
For it's very hard to think things up
When a fairy is about.

And I'd hate to lose my wishes,
For fairies fly away,
And perhaps I'd never have a chance
On any other day.

So I keep three wishes ready,
Lest I should chance to meet,
Any day a fairy
Coming down the street.

ANNETTE WYNNE

## NIGHT DANCERS

*Some people say that there are no fairies, but people*
*who have eyes to see and ears to hear can point out*
*any number of signs that there are fairies all around us.*

THEIR quick feet pattered on the grass
    As light as dewdrops fall.
I saw their shadows on the glass
    And heard their voices call.

But when I went out hurrying
    To join them, they were gone.
I only found a little ring
    Of footprints on the lawn.

THOMAS KENNEDY

21

# HALLOWE'EN

*"Hallowe'en" means "blessed evening." It is the night when the dead are supposed to rise from their graves and walk the earth; and witches ride at moon-rise. So beware!*

Bolt and bar the front door,
  Draw the curtains tight;
Wise folk are in before
  Moon-rise to-night.

*Hallowe'en, Hallowe'en,*
  *Chestnuts to roast,*
*A gift for the fairy,*
  *A prayer for the ghost.*

Who will have their fate told,
  This night is known,
Whose hand is full of gold,
  Who goes alone.

*Hallowe'en, Hallowe'en,*
  *Snapdragon blue,*
*A lover for me*
  *And a fortune for you*

Stars shiver blue and green,
  Moon's wide and white;
There, tattered clouds between,
  Witches take flight.

*Hallowe'en, Hallowe'en,*
  *Apples a-bob,*
*Elves at the key-hole*
  *And imps on the hob.*

"Twelve," calls the deep bell
  To the hollow night.
"Twelve," whisper steeple tops
  Far out of sight.

*Hallowe'en, Hallowe'en,*
  *Fires burn high.*
*Who shall say certainly,*
  *Who can tell truthfully,*
*What solemn company*
  *Passes through the sky?*

MOLLY CAPES

23

## GODMOTHER

*What a fortunate old lady was Godmother! Wouldn't it be convenient to have three faces — or even two? This old lady would probably be a pleasant person to meet at a party.*

THERE was an old lady
Who had three faces,
One for everyday,
And one for wearing places —
To meetings and parties,
Dull places like that —
A face that looked well
With a grown-up hat.

But she carried in her pocket
The face of an elf,
And she'd clap it on quick
When she felt like herself.
Sitting in the parlor
Of somebody's house,
She'd reach in her pocket
Sly as a mouse . . .
And there in the corner,
Sipping her tea,
Was a laughing elf-woman
Nobody could see!

PHYLLIS B. MORDEN

25

# WHO'S IN?

*In every house there are many families. You think that your family is the only one; but if you keep your eyes and ears open, you will learn that you live in a regular apartment house with families in the cellar, under the porch, and in the attic.*

"THE door is shut fast
     And everyone's out."
But people don't know
What they're talking about!

Says the fly on the wall,
And the flame on the coals,
And the dog on his rug,
And the mice in their holes,
And the kitten curled up,
And the spiders that spin —
"What, everyone out?
Why, everyone's in!"

ELIZABETH FLEMING

## THE BAD KITTENS

*It is no wonder that a black cat is supposed to be a
witch's favorite companion.  If there is anything that
looks like a goblin, it is a black cat with its green eyes
shining in the dark.  Do you ever suspect your cat of
keeping tryst with goblins?  What is a tryst?*

You may call, you may call,
But the little black cats won't hear you;
The little black cats are maddened
By the bright green light of the moon.
They are running and whirling and hiding,
They are wild who were once so confiding,
They are mad when the moon is riding —
You will not catch the kittens soon!

They care not for saucers of milk;
They care not for pillows of silk;
Your softest, crooningest call
Means less than the buzzing of flies.
They are seeing more than you see,
They are hearing more than you hear,
And out of the darkness they peer,
With a goblin light in their eyes!

ELIZABETH COATSWORTH

28

# THE MILKMAN

*Some of the world's workers begin their toil when other people still have several hours to sleep. The milkman is one of the earliest risers, and he sees much that is strange and lovely. Have you ever seen the dawn reaping the golden meadows with her flaming sickle?*

WHEN the one o'clock cock begins to crow
    They drag him out of a dream,
And he stares at the stars in the Milky Way
    And the meteors made of cream.

When the sky is a meadow of molten oats
    Sickled with flaming steel,
He hitches his horse to a cart of cans
    With a squeak in its wheezy wheel,

And under the twinkle of sundry suns
    And miscellaneous moons,
His rattling bottles in sleepy lanes
    Tinkle their lonely tunes.

LEONARD J. FEENEY

## THE MOUSE

*Of course no careful housewife would deliberately en-*
*courage the little gray mouse as a regular guest, but*
*who could resist this sad complaint?*

I HEARD a mouse
    Bitterly complaining
In a crack of moonlight
Aslant on the floor—

"Little I ask,
And that little is not granted;
There are few crumbs
In this world any more.

"The bread box is tin
And I cannot get in.

"The jam's in a jar
My teeth cannot mar.

"The cheese sits by itself
On the ice-box shelf.

"All night I run
Searching and seeking;
All night I run
About on the floor.

"Moonlight is there
And a bare place for dancing,
But no little feast
Is spread any more."

ELIZABETH COATSWORTH

31

# MICE

*Contrary to the usual opinion with regard to mice,
Rose Fyleman says that she likes them. Perhaps Eng-
lish mice are more attractive than ours, or perhaps
Miss Fyleman just feels sorry for them.*

I THINK mice
   Are rather nice.

Their tails are long,
Their faces small,
They haven't any
Chins at all.
Their ears are pink,
Their teeth are white,
They run about
The house at night.
They nibble things
They shouldn't touch,
And no one seems
To like them much.

But I think mice
Are nice.

ROSE FYLEMAN

## My Dog

*Puppies certainly can cause a good deal of trouble until they have been properly trained, but it is very difficult to scold them even when they do track up the house or eat somebody's shoes.*

His nose is short and scrubby;
    His ears hang rather low;
And he always brings the stick back,
    No matter how far you throw.

He gets spanked rather often
 For things he shouldn't do,
Like lying-on-beds, and barking,
 And eating up shoes when they're new.

He always wants to be going
 Where he isn't supposed to go.
He tracks up the house when it's snowing—
 Oh, puppy, I love you so!

MARCHETTE GAYLORD CHUTE

## I Heard a Bird Sing

*Read this poem three times and you will know it by heart—and isn't it a pleasant poem to remember?*

I HEARD a bird sing
 In the dark of December
A magical thing
 And sweet to remember.

"We are nearer to Spring
 Than we were in September,"
I heard a bird sing
 In the dark of December.

OLIVER HERFORD

# GARDEN SONG

*Some people plan their gardens especially to attract birds and butterflies. The hummingbird likes flowers with deep cups. The ruby throat of a hummingbird or the frail white wings of a butterfly are a lovely sight just above the tall blue larkspurs. Bee-balm is a brilliantly colored flower with a fringed cup.*

Bee-balm for humming-birds,
    Roses for the bee,
Larkspur for butterflies
    And hollyhocks for me;
Blue flax for orioles
    To mend their hanging nests,
But bee-balm for humming-birds,
    Our ever-welcome guests.

ARTHUR GUITERMAN

# THE SNARE

*The trap is one of the cruelest devices that man uses to hunt wild animals. It is bad enough to think of a lion or a tiger suffering in a trap, but the thought of a little soft rabbit caught by the paw is very sad indeed. Can you feel the anxious sympathy in this poem?*

I HEAR a sudden cry of pain!
 There is a rabbit in a snare;
Now I hear the cry again,
 But I cannot tell from where.

But I cannot tell from where
 He is calling out for aid;
Crying on the frightened air,
 Making everything afraid.

36

Making everything afraid,
   Wrinkling up his little face,
As he cries again for aid;
   And I cannot find the place!

And I cannot find the place
   Where his paw is in the snare;
Little one!  Oh, little one!
   I am searching everywhere.

JAMES STEPHENS

## WIND IS A CAT

*Poets have compared the wind to a great variety of
things, but comparing it to a cat is something new.
Have you ever heard the wind lash its tail or purr?*

Wind is a cat
      That prowls at night,
Now in a valley,
   Now on a height,

Pouncing on houses
   Till folks in their beds
Draw all the covers
   Over their heads.

It sings to the moon,
　　It scratches at doors;
It lashes its tail
　　Around chimneys and roars.

It claws at the clouds
　　Till it fringes their silk;
It laps up the dawn
　　Like a saucer of milk;

Then, chasing the stars
　　To the tops of the firs,
Curls down for a nap
　　And purrs and purrs.

ETHEL ROMIG FULLER

38

# LONDON RAIN

*Don't you enjoy the names of London streets? Remember "Pippin Hill" in the Mother Goose book, and "The Boy Who Lived in Pudding Lane"?*

WHEN it rained in Devon,
   Salt was on my lips;
I leaned against a gray wharf
And dreamed of old ships.

When it rained in Yorkshire,
I tarried indoors
And heard the weather calling
Up and down the moors.

But when it rained in London,
I couldn't stay still;
My feet, before I told them,
Had run to Pippin Hill.

Before I even knew it,
As wet as sops, my feet
Were splashing Dark Horse Alley
And Pickled Herring Street.

Through Pudding Court I paddled,
I waded Honey Lane —
The rain that falls on London
Is not like other rain.

Wet days are wild in Cornwall,
In Kent they're sweet and slow,
But when it rains in London,
Ah, when it rains in London,
You're drenched with long ago.

NANCY BYRD TURNER

## SNOW ADVENT

*Rain often begins with a sharp patter, but snow usually comes very softly. Can you see the picture — the wind brushing up the clouds, the brook held down by ice, and then the sudden coming of the "white bees of the moon"?*

THE clouds were all brushed up and back
    The wrong way by the wind;
The trees were attitudes in black;
The brooks were disciplined.

41

Then soft as spider on a shelf,
Or satin mouse at birth,
Or as a pigeon lends itself
Reluctantly to earth —


No louder than the silken sound
Of the web's silver wheel,
Spraying the darkness all around
With spokes of silken steel —


As soft and softer than all these
Parted the sky at noon;
And the air stood up league-deep in bees,
The white bees of the moon.

JOSEPH AUSLANDER

## BRITTLE WORLD

*When you read this poem, you can almost hear the
sharp tinkle of breaking icicles and see the beautiful
ghostly world after a winter storm.*

BRITTLE the snow on the gables,
    The sleet-hung pines, the night
Sprinkled with stars that quiver
    Over the waste of white.

Fragile the earth in the moonlight,
  The glassy sheet of lake;
If I tapped it with a hammer,
  The brittle world would break.

LEW SARETT

43

# February Twilight

*Sara Teasdale loved stars. She wrote a great many poems about them. This one reminds us of the famous song "O Thou Sublime Sweet Evening Star."*

I STOOD beside a hill
  Smooth with new-laid snow,
A single star looked out
  From the cold evening glow.

There was no other creature
  That saw what I could see—
I stood and watched the evening star
  As long as it watched me.

SARA TEASDALE

44

# STARS

*Here is a curious fancy about the stars. One sun, one moon — but how lavish God was with stars! Before He made man, He filled the heavens with stars that man might see and wonder.*

AND then
He made the stars also.
What a gesture!
What a lovely after-thought!
He made them on a whim,
A tiny fancy.


With trembling eagerness
And all absorbed,
Carelessly profligate,
He made stars by the hundred million thousands,
Like grains of golden pollen.


Then, when He had done, He dropped
Into a maker's dream,
For in His mind was growing
The strange whim of man.

Goldenly slipped from His dreaming hands,
Worlds fell,
As coins through the fingers of a spendthrift.

FLORENCE S. EDSALL

## THE STARLIGHTER

*Robert Louis Stevenson told us of Leerie, the old lamplighter whom he knew as a child in Edinburgh. Arthur Guiterman thinks that there's a starlighter, too, for the lamps of heaven.*

WHEN the bat's on the wing and the bird's
    in the tree,
Comes the starlighter, whom none may see.

First in the West where the low hills are,
He touches his wand to the Evening Star.

Then swiftly he runs on his rounds on high,
Till he's lit every lamp in the dark blue sky.

ARTHUR GUITERMAN

# THE FALLING STAR

*Here is another of Sara Teasdale's star poems.  Did you ever make a wish on a falling star?  Some people say that the wish will surely come true.*

I saw a star slide down the sky,
  Blinding the north as it went by,
Too burning and too quick to hold,
Too lovely to be bought or sold,
Good only to make wishes on
And then forever to be gone.

SARA TEASDALE

# NIGHT

*This is a poem to learn. You probably have learned "The Coin," by the same author. Every one of Miss Teasdale's poems sings itself into our memory.*

STARS over snow,
     And in the west a planet
Swinging below a star —
   Look for a lovely thing and
     you will find it,
It is not far —
   It never will be far.

SARA TEASDALE

# REFLECTION

*"Meditate on beauty." Sara Teasdale told us the same thing when she spoke of the "safe-kept memory of a lovely thing." Cherish beauty, and it shall be doubled. What lovely things have you "safe-kept" in your memory?*

Beauty is a lily,
Sparkling and cool,
Its bowl of dewy petals
Stemming in a pool.

Meditate on beauty,
Hold it, and look! —
Beauty shall be doubled, —
A lily in a brook.

LEW SARETT

49

## I Heard It in the Valley

*If there were no winter, we could never know the wonderful thrill that comes when we hear the first sounds of spring. We hear spring before we see it, probably because the birds know spring is coming long before we do.*

I HEARD it in the valley,
I heard it in the glen;
Listen, children, surely, surely
Spring is coming back again!

I heard it in the valley,
I heard it on the hill,
I heard it where the bare trees stand,
Very brave and still.

I heard it in the valley—
I heard the waters start,
I heard it surely, surely,
I heard it in my heart!

ANNETTE WYNNE

# BIBLE STORIES

*When you grow older and have children of your own, some of your happiest memories will probably be of the times when your mother opened the big Bible and told you the lovely old tales of David, the shepherd boy, and of the carpenter's shop in Nazareth.*

THE room was low and small and kind;
    And in its cupboard old,
The shells were set out to my mind;
    The cups I loved with rims of gold.


Then, with that good gift which she had,
    My mother showed at will,
David, the ruddy Syrian lad,
    With his few sheep upon a hill;


A shop down a rude country street,
    The chips strewn on the floor,
And faintly keen across the heat;
    The simple kinsfolk at the door;

Mary amid the homely din,
   As slim as violet;
The little Jesus just within,
   About His father's business set.

My mother rose, and then I knew
   As she stood smiling there,
Her gown was of that gentle blue
   Which she had made the Virgin wear.

How far the very chairs were grown!
   The gilt rose on each back,
Into a Syrian rose was blown,
   And not our humble gold and black.

That week long, in our acres old,
   Lad David did I see;
From out our cups with rims of gold,
   The little Jesus supped with me.

LIZETTE WOODWORTH REESE

# JUNIPER

*The juniper tree is an evergreen bearing bluish berry-like cones with a warm, pungent taste. The word "juniper" is a pretty word. It has a kindly, sheltering sound, hasn't it?*

Who does not love the juniper tree?
The scent of its branches comes back to me,
And ever I think of the Holy Three
Who came to rest by the juniper tree!
Joseph and Mary and little wee Son
Came to rest when the day was done!
And the little Child slept on His Mother's knee
In the shelter sweet of the juniper tree!

EILEEN DUGGAN

54

## WAIT'S CAROL

*In olden England the children who went from door to door singing Christmas carols were called "waits." Wherever they stopped, the people gave them food and presents. The word "good-den" means "Good greeting" or "God's blessing."*

GIVE ye good-den,
　　Sweet gentlemen,
　　And comely ladies, too.
Give ye good-den,
For once again
　　The Lord Christ comes to you.

By moor and street,
His holy feet
　　Shall pass upon the way,
And give good-den
To beasts and men,
　　For this is Christmas Day.

Ye gentle poor,
Set wide the door
　　So He may enter in.

Bring cup and plate
With simple state,
   And let the feast begin.

And ye who hold
The purse of gold,
   Come out and spend and pray,
And give good-den
To beggar men
   For that it's Christmas Day.

                        BARBARA YOUNG

## I'M WISHING THE WHOLE WORLD CHRISTMAS

*Christmas morning is usually one of the happiest times of the whole year. We feel so gay and contented that our happiness spills over onto everyone else. It's a pity that the feeling doesn't always last longer, isn't it?*

I'M WISHING the whole world Christmas —
   The children, the beasts, and the birds;
I'm wishing the whole world Christmas —
And I'd like to have magical words
To wish just the shining wish I would wish
In the Christmas words I would say,

For I'm wishing the whole world Christmas,
And joy on Christmas Day.


O, I'd need a pen to write golden,
The goldenest pen indeed,
To wish the whole world Christmas
For the happy children to read.
I'm wishing the whole world Christmas
And may the dear Lord be kind,
And send blessings down like snowflakes
For all of His children to find. . . .

ANNETTE WYNNE

## WELCOME TO THE NEW YEAR

*Eleanor Farjeon is an English writer. Every one of
her books is a delight. Don't miss the "Martin
Pippin" stories or anything else that bears her name.
She is a granddaughter of the great actor Joseph
Jefferson, who was famous for his "Rip Van Winkle."*

HEY, my lad, ho, my lad!
    Here's a New Broom.
Heaven's your housetop
    And Earth is your room.

Tuck up your shirtsleeves,
  There's plenty to do —
Look at the muddle
  That's waiting for you!

Dust in the corners
  And dirt on the floor,
Cobwebs still clinging
  To window and door.

Hey, my lad! ho, my lad!
  Nimble and keen —
Here's your New Broom, my lad!
  See you sweep clean.

ELEANOR FARJEON

# PART TWO

But I could go and find her,
Because I'm gypsy, too."   (*Page 62*)

# CHANGELING

*People used to believe that fairies sometimes stole children from their cradles and left fairies instead. They called such children "changelings." A changeling would have a hard time doing dull, everyday tasks. No wonder a changeling escaped sometimes to play with trolls and leprechauns and the rest of the fairy folk. Do you know any people who might perhaps be changelings?*

S HE was a stately lady,
  And kept her in her place
Beside her lord and husband,
  In broideries and lace.

She stepped with pretty hauteur
  In pavan and quadrille.
(But once she skipped with urchins
  At moonrise on the hill.)

She crooned her plaintive ditties
  In verses prim and quaint;
Her lord and husband harkened
  And blest her for a saint.

She was a gracious lady,
  Serene to look upon.
(One night she plotted mischief
  With troll and leprechaun.)

She kept the castle strictly —
  The butlers and the maids;
Went all in white o' mornings,
  And wove her hair in braids.

She walked to church sedately
  And bent her down and prayed.
(But some one saw her follow
  Where gypsy folk had strayed.)

The day before last April
  She buttoned on her shoon
And off she went a-running,
  All in the afternoon.

And where-at-all she ended,
  Why, no one ever knew.
(But I could go and find her,
  Because I'm gypsy, too.)

BARBARA YOUNG

# TARANTELLA

*A tarantella is a kind of lilting dance that delights the
people of Spain and Italy. You can feel the swing and
the beat of the tarantella in this poem, which recalls
happy, carefree days that will never come again for
the two people who danced at the inn.*

DO YOU remember an Inn,
    Miranda?
Do you remember an Inn?
And the tedding and the spreading
Of the straw for a bedding,
And the fleas that tease in the High Pyr-
    enees,
And the wine that tasted of the tar?

And the cheers and the jeers of the
    young muleteers
 (Under the vine of the dark verandah) —
Do you remember an Inn, Miranda?
Do you remember an Inn?
And the cheers and the jeers of the young
    muleteers
Who hadn't got a penny
And who weren't paying any,
And the hammer at the doors and the din?
And the Hip! Hop! Hap!
Of the clap
Of the hands to the twirl and the swirl
Of the girl gone chancing,
Glancing,
Dancing,
Backing and advancing,
Snapping of the clapper to the spin
Out and in —
And the ting, tong, tang of the Guitar!
Do you remember an Inn, Miranda?
Do you remember an Inn?

Never more, Miranda;
Never more.

Only the high peaks hoar;
And Aragon torrent at the door.
No sound
In the walls of the Halls where falls
The tread
Of the feet of the dead to the ground.
No sound:
But the boom
Of the far Waterfall like Doom.

HILAIRE BELLOC

# A Caravan from China Comes

*Mr. Le Gallienne wrote this poem with the oriental
feeling for beauty of sound and color — like Hafiz,
who was a great Persian poet of the olden days. Attar
is essence of roses, and myrrh is a spicy gum not un-
like that which you sometimes find clinging to the
bark of trees. Look into the sky some night and you
will see this fragrant caravan, with the Pleiades making a starry necklace for the moon.*

A caravan from China comes;
　　For miles it sweetens all the air
With fragrant silks and dreaming gums,
　　Attar and myrrh —
A caravan from China comes.

O merchant, tell me what you bring,
　　With music sweet of camel bells;
How long have you been travelling
　　With these sweet smells?
O merchant, tell me what you bring.

A lovely lady is my freight,
　　A lock escaped of her long hair, —

That is this perfume delicate
    That fills the air —
A lovely lady is my freight.

Her face is from another land,
    I think she is no mortal maid, —
Her beauty, like some ghostly hand,
    Makes me afraid;
Her face is from another land.

The little moon my cargo is,
    About her neck the Pleiades
Clasp hands and sing: Hafiz, 'tis this
    Perfumes the breeze —
The little moon my cargo is.

RICHARD LE GALLIENNE

## Palanquin Bearers

*You know what a palanquin is — a kind of chair swinging from poles borne on the shoulders of the bearers. Rich people ride in palanquins. The poor must carry them, but they often sing a lighthearted song as they swing along the dusty road.*

Lightly, O lightly, we bear her along,
    She sways like a flower in the wind of our song;
She skims like a bird on the foam of a stream,
She floats like a laugh from the lips of a dream.

Gaily, O gaily, we glide and we sing,
We bear her along like a pearl on a string.

Softly, O softly, we bear her along,
She hangs like a star in the dew of our song;
She springs like a beam on the brow of the tide,
She falls like a tear from the eyes of a bride;
Lightly, O lightly, we glide and we sing,
We bear her along like a pearl on a string.

SAROJINI NAIDU

## IN THE BAZAARS OF HYDERABAD

*There is probably no more colorful spot in the world
than an Indian bazaar. In this poem Madame Naidu
makes us experience all the sights, sounds, and odors
of the busy market.*

WHAT do you sell, O ye merchants?
Richly your wares are displayed.
*Turbans of crimson and silver,*
*Tunics of purple brocade,*
*Mirrors with panels of amber,*
*Daggers with handles of jade.*

What do you weigh, O ye vendors?
*Saffron and lentil and rice.*
What do you grind, O ye maidens?
*Sandalwood, henna, and spice.*
What do you call, O ye pedlars?
*Chessmen and ivory dice.*


What do you make, O ye goldsmiths?
*Wristlet and anklet and ring,*
*Bells for the feet of blue pigeons,*
*Frail as a dragon-fly's wing,*

*Girdles of gold for the dancers,*
*Scabbards of gold for the king.*

What do you cry, O ye fruitmen?
*Citron, pomegranate, and plum.*
What do you play, O musicians?
*Cithar, sarangi, and drum.*
What do you chant, O magicians?
*Spells for æons to come.*

What do you weave, O ye flower-girls
With tassels of azure and red?
*Crowns for the brow of a bridegroom,*
*Chaplets to garland his bed,*
*Sheets of white blossoms new-gathered*
*To perfume the sleep of the dead.*

SAROJINI NAIDU

# FROM THE HILLS OF DREAM

*It is just before you go to sleep, in that shadowy land
between asleep and awake, that you slowly climb the
Hills of Dream and meet the Host of Faerie.*

ACROSS the silent stream
　　Where the slumber-shadows go,
From the dim blue Hills of Dream
　　I have heard the west wind blow.

Who hath seen that fragrant land,
　　Who hath seen that unscanned west?
Only the listless hand
　　And the unpulsing breast.

But when the west wind blows
　　I see moon-lances gleam
Where the Host of Faerie flows
　　Athwart the Hills of Dream.

And a strange song I have heard
　　By a shadowy stream,
And the singing of a snow-white bird
　　On the Hills of Dream.

FIONA MACLEOD

72

# THE VALLEY OF WHITE POPPIES

*On the other side of the Hills of Dream is the Valley of White Poppies. Notice the lack of color in this poem. Every word contributes to the effect of silence and mystery.*

BETWEEN the grey pastures and the dark wood
A valley of white poppies is lit by the low
   moon:
   It is the grave of dreams, a holy rood.

It is quiet there: no wind doth ever fall.
Long, long ago a wind sang once a heart-sweet
   rune.
   Now the white poppies grow, silent and tall.

A white bird floats there like a drifting leaf:
It feeds upon faint sweet hopes and perishing
   dreams
   And the still breath of unremembering grief.

And as a silent leaf the white bird passes,
Winnowing the dusk by dim forgetful streams.
   I am alone now among the silent grasses.

                                        FIONA MACLEOD

73

# The Moon's Funeral

*Hilaire Belloc has an odd, eerie sense of humor.*
*Don't try to find out exactly what this poem means.*
*Probably the poet didn't know. Just enjoy the de-*
*lightful sounds of the words and remember that the*
*moon still rises.*

THE Moon is dead. I saw her die.
   She in a drifting cloud was drest;
She lay along the uncertain west,
A dream to see.

And very low she spake to me:
"I go where none may understand,
I fade into the nameless land,
And there must lie perpetually."
And therefore I,
And therefore loudly, loudly I
And high
And very piteously make cry:
"The Moon is dead.  I saw her die."

And will she never rise again?
The Holy Moon?  Oh, never more!
Perhaps along the inhuman shore
Where pale ghosts are
Beyond the low lethean fen
She and some wide infernal star . .
To us who loved her never more,
The Moon will never rise again.
Oh! never more in nightly sky
Her eye so high shall peep and pry
To see the great world rolling by.
For why?
The Moon is dead.  I saw her die.

HILAIRE BELLOC

75

## FOG, THE MAGICIAN

*Fog interests the poets almost as much as the mysteri-
ous moon. Fog is a kind of magician, for it makes
many changes in the appearance of the world. Can
you see why the poet compares the world emerging
from fog to God's work of creation?*

WRAPPED in a cloak
Of grey mystery,
Fog, the magician,
Steals tip-toe out of the sea.
In seven-league boots
He skims across the sky,
Blowing out the sun,
Blotting out the blue.

On cobweb wires he slides to earth,
Glides through gardens surreptitiously,
And sponges every color out of flowers.
Churches, houses, trees,
He wipes like chalky outlines from a
    board.

Fog says — "Presto!"
And birds turn into nothing as they fly,
Men grow vague and vanish.
Fog claps his hands!
And motor-cars roll off into a void,
Dogs evaporate,
Cats dissolve to bodiless meows.

Noiselessly, peacefully,
The old world ends.
Nothing remains
But fog and me
And another world to be.
Slowly, dimly,
I seem to feel
A little of the wonder and the joy
That must have gladdened God in the be-
    ginning —
Creation before Him.

                    MELVILLE CANE

# CARAVANS

*Here are caravans of a different kind. Man's slow thinking to find the way out of ignorance and superstition is something like caravans pushing on across the centuries.*

GREAT, grey caravans moving in the night,
    Full of sullen mystery, laden down with
heavy things;
Crowding through the darkness as they push on
    toward the light;
    Great, grey caravans, on great, grey wings.

Swift, silent caravans smashing through the night,
    Plunging over trackless wastes, wastes where
    trails can never meet,
Spraying noiseless gravel as they crowd on out of
    sight:
    Swift, silent caravans on swift, silent feet.

Soft, slow caravans swaying through the night,
    Tinkling bells and padded feet, and spices that
      the traders bought,
Easing through the moonlight, over sands dull
      white:
    Soft, slow caravans of soft, slow thought.

HAL BORLAND

## SMALL RAIN

*Someone said that the ten loveliest words in the language are these: lullaby, tranquil, murmur, chimes, melody, glisten, luminous, golden, mist, dawn. Alice Lawry Gould thought that it would be an interesting experiment to weave them into a sonnet. This is the result. Make a list of lovely words yourself. Perhaps you could even make them into a poem. Some words appeal to the ear and some to the eye, and some we like for their meaning. You may want to make three different lists.*

NO LULLABY is older than the rain:
    The small rain falling on the tender grass.
The Hebrew shepherd lad, the Lesbian lass,
Hushed by its tranquil murmuring have lain
And dreamed their dreams. The nations rise
    and wane,
The destinies of men and empires pass;

But still tonight upon my window glass
Thin chimes tap out their slumber-song again.

I hear it falling, falling through the night—
The ancient rain that makes the worn earth
    new—
Knowing that when both rain and night are
    gone,
Most gently will the fingers of first light
Wake birds to melody, and glisten through
The luminous and golden mist of dawn.

ALICE LAWRY GOULD

## NIGHT CLOUDS

*Here is the moon again — and what a transformation!*
*See the colors — gold, green, vermilion! What would*
*the poets do without the moon?*

THE white mares of the moon rush along the
    sky
Beating their golden hoofs upon the glass heavens;
The white mares of the moon are all standing on
    their hind legs
Pawing at the green porcelain doors of the re-
mote heavens.

Fly, mares!
Strain your utmost,
Scatter the milky dust of stars,
Or the tiger sun will leap upon you and destroy
　　you
With one lick of his vermilion tongue.

AMY LOWELL

## Summer Shower

*Here is a poem that uses words like colors from a paintbox. Your eyes see color, and your ears hear music. Which would you choose as the loveliest words you know?*

THUNDERING, shimmering, silvery gray,
It's raining today,
Shining and slanting
Spears, such a shower as we've been wanting.

Freesia and fuchsia and mignonette
And violet
And golden glow
And blue delphinium, row on row,

And morning glory and hollyhock
And four-o'clock
And sweet alyssum
And bachelor button and cucumber blossom
And black-eyed susan and purple clover,
When the rain's over,
Will shake the shower
Out of each brimming, glistening flower

And the sun will turn to a bright metal
Each bright petal;
When the rain's done
Each leaf and each petal will sparkle in the sun.

SELMA ROBINSON

## TWO SEWING

*Hazel Hall has made a charming little whimsey that tells us how Spring's lovely clothes are made. The wind is a very good dressmaker.*

THE wind is sewing with needles of
 rain;
With shining needles of rain
It stitches into the thin
Cloth of earth — in,
In, in, in.

*Oh, the wind has often sewed with
  me!*—
*One, two, three.*

Spring must have fine things
To wear, like other springs.
Of silken green the grass must be
Embroidered. *One and two and three.*

Then every crocus must be made
So subtly as to seem afraid
Of lifting color from the ground;
And after crocuses, the round
Heads of tulips and all the fair
Intricate garb that Spring will wear.
The wind must sew with needles of rain,
With shining needles of rain
Stitching into the thin
Cloth of earth — in,
In, in, in —
For all the springs of futurity.
*One, two, three.*

HAZEL HALL

# Traveling Storm

*Here are wind and rain in a menacing mood. There are good descriptions here — "black with the speeding storm," "a swift dark wind." You can almost feel the steaming heat and then the sharp, cool wind.*

THE sky above us here is open again.
  The sun comes hotter, and the shingles
    steam,
The trees are done with dripping, and the hens
Bustle among bright pools to pick and drink.
But east and south are black with the speeding
    storm.
That thunder, low and far, remembering noth-
    ing,
Gathers a new world under it and growls,
Worries, strikes, and is gone. Children at win-
    dows
Cry at the rain, it pours so heavily down,
Drifting across the yard till the sheds are gray.
A county farther on, the wind is all —
A swift dark wind that turns the maples pale,
Ruffles the hay, and spreads the swallows' wings.

Horses, suddenly restless, are unhitched,
And men, with glances upward, hurry in;
Their overalls blow full and cool; they shout;
Soon they will lie in barns and laugh at the light-
ning.
Another county yet, and the sky is still;
The air is fainting; women sit with fans
And wonder when a rain will come that way.

MARK VAN DOREN

## MARCH DREAMS

*The winds are Nature's brooms, and March is the
time for house cleaning. City streets and country
meadows must be ready for the spring.*

Winds of March, come sweeping through the
long, brown valley.
Winds of March, ride flying through the dull,
bare town.
Toss the crimsoned maples where the sodden
leaves are lying,
Brush the yellowed mosses of the hills' gray gown.
Through the snow-banked meadow silent brooks
are stealing.

Silver grasses shimmer where the bowed hedge
  sleeps.
Mist along the mountain slopes and white clouds
  wheeling;
Blurs of purple shadow that the brown wood
  keeps.

Winds of March, the lilies in the brick-bound
  gardens
Are lifting slender fingers through the sun
  warmed sod.
And down the dingy parkway a dim ghost lingers,
A crumpled wraith of greenness like a twisted
  pagan god.

Winds of road and hilltop, breathe upon our
    dullness.
Winds of wood and ocean, sweep our sooty
    squares.
Some place in our dreaming there are rows of
    purple iris
Where a March wind frolics and a March sun
    flares.

ROSE HENDERSON

## OUT IN THE WOOD

*There is a springlike lilt to this poem with its double
rhymes and tiptilting cadences. Spring makes the
poets pipe gay little songs.*

Out in the wood today, oh, such a wonder!
    Greenery over and greenery under;
Rustle of leaves with their tremulous tracery;
Swaying of ferns with their fairylike lacery;
Nodding of blooms with their blue, white, and
    yellow bells;
Over the pebbles brook-trebles like mellow
    bells;
Reed-note of robin and flute-note of vireo,
Jargon of jay and wren chatter so cheery-o;

Never a burden and never a care to see;
Everything blithesome and everything fair to
see;
Every breath magical, every bough lyrical;
Just the unfolding of all the old miracle.


Greenery over and greenery under;
Out in the wood today, oh, such a wonder!

CLINTON SCOLLARD


## To the City in the Snow

*Now down comes the snow to make a fairy world.
"Spinster" and "diadem" and "scintillating" should
send you to your dictionary.*


ON BRICK and stone and trees all stark and
bare
The snow comes softly, swiftly drifting down,
Transforming this prim spinster of a town
Into a sparkling princess passing fair.
With alabaster brow and frosty hair,
And icy jewels in her ermine gown,
She wears the glistening steeples for a crown,
And rears her crystal diadem in the air.

And then the moon sends down a silver beam,
The scintillating stars their sapphires show,
Amber and rose from friendly windows stream,
And multi-colored lights flash to and fro,
Tinting with fairy hue and dancing gleam
The too cold beauty of the fallen snow.

AGNES O'GARA RUGGERI

91

# THE WEAVING

*You remember that Lew Sarett said, "Beauty shall be doubled." There is a similar thought in this poem. This poet wants us to look upward and see, not just the reflection, but also the beauty that caused it.*

THE moon is weaving in the street
A tanglement for passing feet,

That must go always up and down
From the river to the town,

For men walk there who never see
The lovely gestures that a tree

Makes over them when they go by.
These men never see the sky.

Their hearts are heavy and they walk
With timid eyes.  They never talk.

And so the moon is making there,
Out of her shining, beautiful hair,

Reflection of the branches so
That tired, awkward men may know

By looking on the ground they love
What excellent beauty moves above.

HAROLD LEWIS COOK

93

## LEGACY

*Some people might be disappointed at receiving a legacy of "a little sloping acre" instead of jewels or money. Which would you rather have?*

I HAD a rich old great-aunt
Who left me, when she died,
A little sloping acre
And not a thing beside.

Nothing else she left me
But a clump of sweet phlox
And an old silver aspen
And some hollyhocks.

A humming-bird disputed
My heritage with me,
And so did a robin
And a gold-backed bee.

A cricket owned a hummock,
He couldn't say how;
Two wrens held a mortgage
On one aspen bough.

A toad claimed a corner
(He said it was a lease).
We learned to live together
In a sort of cheery peace.

Never such an acre
To mortal was given!
My good old great-aunt,
May she rest in heaven!

                              NANCY BYRD TURNER

# VOICES

*Usually it is the people who live in coastal towns and fishing villages who long to sail away, but sometimes the sea calls to people who have never even seen a towering, white-capped wave. Perhaps some far-off ancestor was a sailor, and through him the sea calls once again.*

THE restless sea is calling, and I would be away
    To where the surf pounds up the beach to
    thunder in my ears,
To where the salt wind tastes like wine, and
    sailing vessels gay
Go out to strange sea-guarded ports and drift
    home gray with years.
From books and shells and scraps of tales these
    thoughts have come to me,
For I was born far inland who long to go to sea.

The midland has its voices, but they call to me in
    vain.
I care not for the whispering road nor drumming
    city street.

My heartbeats do not quicken to the thrush's
joyous strain,
Nor to the sighing music of the wind upon the
wheat.
The bees drone their contented song—but what
is this to me?
For I was born far inland and long to hear the sea.

The sky is like the sea today and clouds like gal-
leons ride—
I found a tiny river just beginning near the
spring,
That called for me to follow and it would be my
guide;
A boisterous echo in its tone, that yet was whispering,
Gave me a hint of ocean surge, and soon I know
that we
Shall leave this inland country and make our way
to sea.

JAMES S. HEARST

# TRAVEL

*Some people are domestic and like to stay at home;
others suffer from wanderlust. The old English poet,
Chaucer, said that in the spring especially we "long to
go on pilgrimages." Do the brightly colored posters
of the travel bureaus make you want to start forth,
too? Where would you go first?*

THE railroad track is miles away,
    And the day is loud with voices speak-
      ing,
Yet there isn't a train goes by all day
    But I hear its whistle shrieking.

All night there isn't a train goes by,
  Though the night is still for sleep and
    dreaming,
But I see its cinders red on the sky,
  And hear its engine steaming.

My heart is warm with the friends I make,
  And better friends I'll not be knowing,
Yet there isn't a train I wouldn't take,
  No matter where it's going.

EDNA ST. VINCENT MILLAY

## THE LIGHTSHIP

*Josephine Johnson is a young writer who has won fame for her novels and short stories. Some people go forth to adventure, but others are like lightships. Someone in the family — often the eldest sister — stays at home, a haven for the others when they come back "beggared or riding deep" with treasure.*

OUT with the tide, beneath the morning sun,
  Along the highways of the wide bright sea
The ships go forth in beauty — even the smallest
  one
Goes forward eagerly!

Only the lightship, lonely, still, and proud,
Swings at her anchor, while a great undertow
Of passionate longing fills her, throbbing through
    keel and shroud,
For ports she may not know . . .

Then the blue dusk drops down, and from afar
The ships return.  Beggared or riding deep,
For each a welcoming haven inside the harbor
    bar,
Furled canvas, quiet sleep.


But sleepless must the lightship lie, and lone
By the sharp reef—no dreams of curious lands,
Great burning unknown stars, bright birds, fan-
    tastic bone
Bleaching on island sands—


Never the voyage!  Never the spreading sail!
Never the swift prow cutting through the foam
Of fabulous silver shorelines—after the fiercest
    gale,
Never the hope of home!


Steadfast and strong above the gathering chill
Her light burns on.  How shall the passing bark
Surmise this desperate hunger?  Lonely and proud
    and still
Are beacons in the dark!

JOSEPHINE JOHNSON

# A SHIP FOR SINGAPORE

*They say that a true sailor can never be content in harbor. When he knows that a ship is sailing, the sea's wild horses call him and even the joys of home cannot hold him — he must be off and away.*

A SHIP is sailing for Singapore!
O heart be swift and latch the door!

My fire burns bright and the shadows fall
In yellow rhythms along the wall.
My love sleeps near and her dreams are deep,
Her lips a rose that has fallen asleep.

The fire burns bright and the candles glow,
And I must not go — I must not go!

There is no peace I can know to-night
Though my love sleeps near and the fire
    burns bright,
For stars will call from an Indian sky
And a gold moon haunt me blowing by.
The sea's wild horses will leap and fly,
Foam on their manes and wind in their eye!

O heart be swift and latch the door —
A ship is sailing for Singapore!

DANIEL WHITEHEAD HICKY

## WHO PILOTS SHIPS

*An engineer or a pilot must have a tremendous sense*
*of power and responsibility, remembering how much*
*depends upon his skill and judgment. The pilot en-*
*joys much of beauty, too, that is denied the engineer.*
*The sea is often lonely, but the pilot sees the beauty*
*and immensity.*

WHO pilots ships knows all a heart can know
Of beauty, and his eyes may close in death

And be content.   There is no wind to blow
Whiter  than  foam-white  wind  and  no  wind's
    breath
Sweeter than tropic wind.   There is no star
That throbs with cold white fire as North stars
    do,
No  golden  moon-path  lovelier  than  the  far
Path burning on the sea when dusk is blue.
There is no rain so swift as rain that flies
In  bright  battalions  with  a  storm  begun,
No song that shakes the heart like amber cries
Of gulls with wings turned yellow in the sun.
Who  pilots  ships,  when  life's  last  heartbeats
    stop,
Has drained the cup of beauty drop by drop.

DANIEL   WHITEHEAD   HICKY

# POLO PLAYER

*If you have ever seen a polo game, even if only in a
news reel, you will realize that the poet has caught
here all the sound, movement, and intense excitement
of a game that is a test of skill and endurance for horse
as well as man.*

SWIFT as an arrow in the wind he goes
   Across the stretching velvet of the grass;
Like sudden music now he leaps and flows
In quickening rhythms as the hoofbeats pass.
They poise in space a fleeting moment, curve
Close to the ground again; now higher, higher,
They take the wind again; they leap, they
      swerve
With all the maddening passion of a fire.
The mallets whiz along the wind, they click
Staccato-like, again they whirr and rise;
Far quicker than the swiftest wind is quick
He sweeps across the field; his squinting eyes
Fast on the ball, he sees it leap and roll . . .
His blood shouts in his veins, the goal, the goal!

DANIEL WHITEHEAD HICKY

# TO AN AVIATOR

*Man has always had dreams of flying. The Greeks told the story of Dædalus and Icarus; Leonardo da Vinci made drawings for a "flying machine." Now that man actually has learned how to ride the wind, will he scorn the earth or will he return to it with gratitude after his flight is done?*

You who have grown so intimate with stars
    And know their silver dripping from your
      wings,
Swept with the breaking day across the sky,
Known kinship with each meteor that swings—

You who have touched the rainbow's fragile gold,
Carved lyric ways through dawn and dusk and
      rain
And soared to heights our hearts have only
      dreamed —
How can you walk earth's common ways again?

DANIEL WHITEHEAD HICKY

## COURAGE

*This poem, by Amelia Earhart, is particularly signifi-
cant in the light of her tragic fate.  Perhaps she would
not have called it tragic.  She made her choice and
dared "the soul's dominion."  No doubt she would
have said the price was not too high.*

COURAGE is the price that life exacts for
      granting peace.
The soul that knows it not, knows no release
From little things;

Knows not the livid loneliness of fear
Nor mountain heights, where bitter joy can hear
The sound of wings.

How can life grant us boon of living, compensate
For dull gray ugliness and pregnant hate
Unless we dare

The soul's dominion?   Each time we make a
    choice, we pay
With courage to behold resistless day
And count it fair.

AMELIA EARHART
1934

## ANTIQUE SHOP

*Long before Carl Carmer became famous for* Stars
Fell on Alabama *and his other novels, he lived for
a while in New Orleans in the section called "French
Town."   There he wrote a number of poems inspired
by its quaintness and charm.   This poem actually
does have a rocking-chair rhythm.*

I KNEW an old lady
  A long time ago
Who rocked while she told me
The things I should know.

She lies in her grave now
And I am a man
But here is her rocker
And here is her fan.

Her fan and her rocker
Are all that remain
But I can still see her
Rock-rocking,
Talk-talking,
Rock-rocking
Again.

CARL CARMER

## The Cathedral of St. Louis

*The Cathedral is old and grey and haunted with
memories. Mr. Carmer shows it to us at early evening
when the Angelus rings and all the people stop and
say their evening prayers.*

I KNOW I shall remember
When it is time to die
Those towers, that cross, at evening
Against the mellow sky.

And life shall leave me lightly
(I shall not know nor care)
Like a chime of bell notes drifting
Across the shadowed square.

CARL CARMER

110

## SLAVE QUARTER

*Other people live now in the old stone quarters where the slaves were kept, but perhaps their ghosts come back and play the banjos once again when moonlight fills the square.*

I CAN hear banjos
  Soft and light
Down in the courtyard
In the moonlight.

What are they playing?
I cannot know,
For players and music
Died long ago.

**CARL CARMER**

111

# INCIDENT

*This is a sad little story of a small colored boy of
eight who went away on a happy visit; then his whole
world was darkened by a cruel word. You know yourself that calling names can hurt. Don't do it to any-
one else and leave unhappy memories.*

ONCE riding in Old Baltimore,
   Heart filled, head filled with glee,
I saw a Baltimorean
Staring straight at me.


Now I was eight and very small,
And he was no whit bigger
And so I smiled, but he
Stuck out his tongue and called me nigger.


I saw the whole of Baltimore
From May until November.
Of all the things that happened there—
That's all that I remember.

COUNTEE CULLEN

# I Have Wrapped My Dreams in a Silken Cloth

*Countee Cullen, a Negro himself and a distinguished gentleman, shows us how the Negro feels. He is usually not bitter, but sad and resigned because of the dreams that he may not cherish.*

I HAVE wrapped my dreams in a silken cloth
And laid them away in a box of gold,
Where long may cling the lips of the moth;
I have wrapped my dreams in a silken cloth.
I hide no hate; I am not even wroth
Who found life's breath so keen and cold.
I have wrapped my dreams in a silken cloth
And laid them away in a box of gold.

COUNTEE CULLEN

113

# AFRICAN DANCE

*Langston Hughes is another brilliant Negro. This poem is really perfect, with its strong, rhythmic beat. Read it in a low, even chant, keeping the beat of the drums in mind. In the third line each of the words "low" and "slow" has four counts.*

THE low beating of the tom-toms,
  The slow beating of the tom-toms,
Low . . . slow
Slow . . . low—
Stirs your blood.

          Dance!
A night-veiled girl
    Whirls softly into a
    Circle of light.
Whirls softly . . . slowly,
Like a wisp of smoke around the fire—
    And the tom-toms beat,
    And the tom-toms beat,
And the low beating of the tom-toms
    Stirs your blood.

LANGSTON HUGHES

# ADMONITIONS

*This poem suggests that we are often more prone to be guided by superstition than by common sense. Do you ever do things that someone has told you to do, not because you really believe in them, but just to be on the safe side?*

My mother said to me,
"Try to be good.
Keep your belongings
Neat as you should.
Say your prayers daily
Before you sleep,
And make no promise
You cannot keep."

My black mammy said to me,
"Thirteen's bad.
Let it alone,
Or you'll wish you had.
Nebber cut yo' vittles
Wid a black-handled knife,
An' doan kill a spider.
Hit's de debbil's wife."

Seldom I'm good
For virtue's sake,
And many's the promise
I've made to break.
But I shun thirteen
And a black-handled knife,
And I couldn't kill a spider,
To save my life.

MARGARET BELL HOUSTON

116

# CRANBERRY ROAD

*It sounds as if the cranberry road must be on Cape
Cod — surely somewhere on the New England coast.
Did you read Rachel Field's story of Hitty, the doll
that went to sea?*

I'D LIKE to be walking the cranberry road,
　Where the sea shines blue through the bris-
　　tling firs,
And the rocky pastures are over-grown
　With bayberry bushes and junipers;
Where orchards of bent old apple-trees
　Go trooping down to the pebbly shore,
And the clapboard houses are seaward turned,
　With larkspur clumps at every door;
Where there's plenty of time to say good-day
　When friendly eyes from a window peer —
Oh, I'd like to be back on the cranberry road;
　I wish I were there instead of here!

RACHEL FIELD

# Shops

*You would probably guess that this is an English poem, or perhaps Irish, since Winifred Letts writes much of Ireland. It makes us think a little differently of the many people who serve us. We call "shops" stores and "stalls" stands, and an "ironmongery" is a hardware store.*

I LIKE the people who keep shops,
  Busy and cheerful folk with friendly faces.
They handle only lovely things — bulbs, seed and
    flowers,
China and glass and gay-backed magazines,
Velvet and satin, foreign silks and laces.


One keeps a stall that's good to see,
Of nuts and fruit the morning sunlight dapples,
With dewy green things fresh from country gar-
    dens,
Tomatoes, bloomy plums and figs in baskets,
Melons and pears, and red or russet apples.

The ironmonger charms me, too,
With wholesome things of house and ground for
      selling,
Rakes, hoes and spades, tinware and tacks and
      hammers,
And shining lamps that wait for kindling fingers,
A pleasant place for converse, good, clean-smell-
      ing.


To serve us seems their only aim,
Asking our wishes, quick to crave our pardon,
And yet I know in each of these shop people
There dwells a soul withdrawn from us, elusive,
The shop can never know — a secret garden.


How can we guess who see them so,
Behind their counters, writing down our orders,
The hidden glades of thought, the fair surprises
That lie without our reach, the blue horizons
Stretching for them beyond their peaceful bor-
      ders?

WINIFRED M. LETTS

## VILLAGE PORTRAIT

*Not all the knowledge in the world is found in books.
Many a "half-wit" knows secrets that the rest of us
have never even guessed. Keep the proper pronunci-
ation of "breeches" here, even though it does not
rhyme exactly with "reaches."*

HE WAS the half-wit of that prairie town,
    The butt of every loafer's jest. His shack
Drowsed in a heap south of the railroad track
Near Perkins' slough. When winter settled down
And blizzards swept across the prairie reaches,
He'd huddle there and feed his fire. The door
Leaked cold. He'd watch the frost crawl on the
    floor
And slap his numb arms down against his
    breeches.

He was the half-wit.  But we boys soon found
No other knew so well where red haws grew,
Or where the black-cased walnuts stained the
      ground,
And when the yellow sunfish bit.  He knew
The thrush's song in spring, and understood
How to trail wild things through a snowy wood.

THOMAS W. DUNCAN

## Courage Has a Crimson Coat

*There is a good deal to think about in this short poem. Why do you think that Courage should wear a crimson coat? Have you ever seen the cap and gown that Knowledge wears or the cloth of gold on some famous king or queen, either real or in the movies? Behind each one of them, however, is some patient mother or sister or aunt weaving their fine robes out of her own self-sacrifice.*

Courage has a crimson coat
    Trimmed with trappings bold,
Knowledge dons a dress of note,
    Fame's is cloth of gold.
Far they ride and fair they roam,
    Much they do and dare;
Gray-gowned Patience sits at home,
    And weaves the stuff they wear.

NANCY BYRD TURNER

## THE PATH TO SHOTTERY

*You have no doubt either seen Cornelia Otis Skinner in recital or heard her over the radio and know that she is a very great actress who can make you laugh or cry at will. Shakespeare wrote the greatest plays of all time; so it is not surprising that Miss Skinner meditates on Will Shakespeare's thoughts as he crossed the fields to Anne Hathaway's cottage in Shottery.*

OVER the fields to Shottery, fresh with a wet-
      green scent,
The path leads through the haws and wheat, the
      path the Poet went.

A skylark staying up too late is fearful to go home,
And blades of grass begin to stir where little
      beetles roam.

What was he musing on the path to twilit Shot-
    tery?
What captive song was in his heart that struggled
    to be free?

Did he know his little candle would forever throw
    its beams,
Did he think the world would tremble at the
    beauty of his dreams?

Or was the Poet wondering, as he chewed a blade
    of grass,
If he should walk that night with Anne or choose
    some Stratford lass?

CORNELIA OTIS SKINNER

# THE MIRROR

*Here is a pretty problem for you. Why do you see a fool when you look into a mirror and a wise man when you see yourself in a pool?*

WHEN I look into a glass
    Myself's my only care;
But I look into a pool
    For all the wonders there.

When I look into a glass
    I see a fool;
But I see a wise man
    When I look into a pool.

WILLIAM H. DAVIES


# DUST OF SNOW

*Even when a whole day seems spoiled because of something we are sorry about, some simple touch of natural beauty will often set things right again.*

THE way a crow
    Shook down on me

The dust of snow
 From a hemlock tree

Has given my heart
 A change of mood
And saved some part
 Of a day I had rued.

ROBERT FROST

## PROOF

*Many people refuse to believe in God because they
cannot see Him. The poet wonders here why we ac-
cept so readily the miracles of science, which after all
are made only by man, and even doubt for an instant
that God can hear our prayers.*

IF RADIO's slim fingers
 Can pluck a melody
From night and toss it over
 A continent or sea;
If songs, like crimson roses,
 Are culled from thin, blue air,
Why should mortals wonder
 If God can hear their prayer?

ETHEL ROMIG FULLER

126

## SHADOWS

*Here is a cheerful poem to remind us of something that we often forget. It takes a little shadow to make us remember the sun.*

A DARK, elusive shadow—
    Trailing my pleasant way
Through thronging street, and meadow
    All on a summer's day.

But what care I for shadows!
    Of substance, they have none;
And he who casts the shadows
    Is walking in the sun!

ARTHUR J. PEEL

## GOSSIP

*People often do not realize how cruel gossip can be until it touches them. Have you ever been in a group when you held your breath lest something unkind be said about you or someone you love? It's a very unhappy feeling.*

BEFORE I knew how cruel
   Just common talk can be,
I thought that words were singing things
   With colors like the sea.

But since I've felt their caustic lash,
   And know how they can sting,
I hold my breath when words go by
   For fear they will not sing.

LEXIE DEAN ROBERTSON

# I Bid You Keep Some Few Small Dreams

*Sometime when you want very much to have something that you ought to wait for until you are older, read this poem. It is very hard for parents to refuse what their children ask, but they do not want you to use up all the lovely experiences in life before you are old enough to enjoy or appreciate them. It is surprising how things lose their thrill as soon as we possess them.*

I PRAY that you may never have
    The things you long for most,
For he who gratifies desire
    Must pay a princely cost.

The world was spread out at my feet;
    It spelled romance to me;
I spent ten years in travel —
    Now there's nothing left to see.

The doll I wanted as a child
    Seemed strangely wonderful,
Until I held her in my arms —
    Then she was just a doll.

The things we long for give to life
  The purpose and the gleam.
The things we get, however fine,
  Are never what they seem.

O rather would I bid you keep
  A few small dreams in trust,
Than see you have the things you want
  And watch them turn to dust.

HELEN FRAZEE-BOWER

## Misdirection

*Many a good mechanic has been spoiled because his
parents wanted him to be a doctor or a lawyer. That
which is useful and serves mankind is also beautiful;
so do not be ashamed to serve the world with your
hands if that is your gift.*

I SHAPE the vessel of my life,
    Hammer it cold, hammer it hot.
I try my best to make of it
    What it is not.

Blow, bellows, blow;
    Burn, fire, burn —
I try to shape a silver vase
    Out of a copper urn.

                ELEANOR SLATER

# THE LIEN

*Too many people in this world are busy with foolish, unimportant affairs, forgetting that the "prior claim upon our days" is to love God, to obey Him, and to serve Him in whatever state of life He has placed us.*

RELENTLESS press of little things;
    Eternal haste to do them all;
The prior claim upon our days
Relinquished to the trivial.

Our obligations never paid,
But endless and imperative.
O Life, why must you always leave
So little time to live?

ADELAIDE LOVE

## MADMAN'S SONG

*Perhaps already you have heard the sound of a silver horn. It may be calling you to serve as a doctor, a nurse, or a missionary. Never let your ears grow dull to it; never let the love of money make you long for a golden pillow. The world will call you mad, but don't mind that. Study and work and serve and follow — follow the silver horn.*

BETTER to see your cheek grown hollow,
  Better to see your temple worn,
Than to forget to follow, follow,
After the sound of a silver horn.

Better to bind your brow with willow
And follow, follow until you die,
Than to sleep with your head on a golden
    pillow,
Nor lift it up when the hunt goes by.

Better to see your cheek grown sallow
And your hair grown gray, so soon, so soon,
Than to forget to hallo, hallo,
After the milk-white hounds of the moon.

ELINOR WYLIE

# INDEX OF TITLES

137

# INDEX OF AUTHORS

143

# INDEX OF FIRST LINES

148

# ACKNOWLEDGMENTS

THANKS are due the following authors, publishers, and others, in this country and abroad, by and with whose permission the enumerated copyrighted selections are included:

D. Appleton-Century Company for "Cranberry Road," by Rachel Field, from *St. Nicholas Magazine,* and "Hush Song," by Elizabeth Shane, from *By Bog and Sea in Donegal.*

The Bookman Publishing Company, Inc., for "Caravans," by Hal Borland, and "Night Dancers," by Thomas Kennedy.

Hal Borland for his "Caravans."

Brandt and Brandt for "Travel," by Edna St. Vincent Millay, from *Second April,* published by Harper and Brothers, copyright, 1921, by Edna St. Vincent Millay, reprinted by permission of the author.

Jonathan Cape, Ltd., for "Night Clouds," by Amy Lowell, from *What's O'Clock.*

Molly Capes for her "Hallowe'en."

Carl Carmer for his "Antique Shop," "The Cathedral of St. Louis," and "Slave Quarter," from *French Town.*

*The Christian Science Monitor* for "Small Rain," by Alice Lawry Gould, and "Shadows," by Arthur J. Peel.

Doubleday, Doran and Company, Inc., for "Mice," by Rose Fyleman, from *Fifty-One New Nursery Rhymes,* copyright 1932.

149

W. Collins Sons and Company, Ltd., for "The Wagon in the Barn," by John Drinkwater, and "Who's In?" by Elizabeth Fleming.

*The Commonweal* for "Juniper," by Eileen Duggan; "Godmother," by Phyllis B. Morden; and "To the City in the Snow," by Agnes O'Gara Ruggeri.

Constable and Company, Ltd., for "Little Brother's Secret," by Katharine Mansfield.

Harold Lewis Cook for his "The Weaving."

Coward-McCann, Inc., for "The Bad Kittens" and "The Mouse," by Elizabeth Coatsworth, from *Compass Rose,* copyright, 1929, by Coward-McCann, Inc.

Dodd, Mead and Company, Inc., for "Two Sewing," by Hazel Hall; "A Caravan from China Comes," by Richard Le Gallienne; "The Lien," by Adelaide Love; "From the Hills of Dream," "Hushing Song," and "The Valley of White Poppies," by Fiona Macleod; "Cradle Song," "In the Bazaars of Hyderabad," and "Palanquin Bearers," by Sarojini Naidu; and "Legacy" and "London Rain," by Nancy Byrd Turner.  Each of these selections is used by permission of Dodd, Mead and Company, Inc.

Gerald Duckworth and Company, Ltd., for "The Moon's Funeral" and "Tarantella," by Hilaire Belloc.

Thomas W. Duncan for his "Village Portrait."

E. P. Dutton and Company, Inc., for "Garden Song" and "The Starlighter," by Arthur Guiterman, taken from *Gaily the Troubadour;* "Shops," by Winifred M. Letts, taken from *The Spires of Oxford and Other Poems;* and "Growing Up" and "Wishes," by Edna Kingsley Wallace, taken from *Feelings and Things.* Each of these selections is published and copyrighted by E. P. Dutton and Company, Inc., New York.

Florence S. Edsall for her "Stars."

Eleanor Farjeon for her "Welcome to the New Year," from *Come Christmas.*

Farrar and Rinehart, Inc., for "Bible Stories," by Lizette Woodworth Reese, from *Selected Poems,* copyright, 1926, and "Gentle Name" and "Summer Shower," by Selma Robinson, from *City Child,* copyright, 1931. Each of these selections is reprinted by permission of Farrar and Rinehart, Inc., publishers.

Elizabeth Fleming for her "Who's In?"

Helen Frazee-Bower for her "I Bid You Keep Some Few Small Dreams."

Ethel Romig Fuller for her "Proof" and "Wind Is a Cat."

Harcourt, Brace and Company, Inc., for "Courage," by Amelia Earhart, from *Last Flight,* and "Fog, the Magician," by Melville Cane.

Harper and Brothers for "Snow Advent," by Joseph Auslander, from *No Traveller Returns,* and "I Have Wrapped My Dreams in a Silken Cloth" and "Incident," by Countee Cullen, from *Color.*

George G. Harrap and Company, Ltd., for "Courage," by Amelia Earhart, from *Last Flight*.

James S. Hearst for his "Voices."

William Heinemann, Ltd., for "Cradle Song," "In the Bazaars of Hyderabad," and "Palanquin Bearers," by Sarojini Naidu.

Rose Henderson for her "March Dreams."

Henry Holt and Company, Inc., for "Dust of Snow," by Robert Frost, from *New Hampshire;* "Polo Player," "A Ship for Singapore," "To an Aviator," and "Who Pilots Ships," by Daniel Whitehead Hicky, from *Bright Harbor;* and "Brittle World" and "Reflection," by Lew Sarett, from *Wings against the Moon*.

Margaret Bell Houghton for her "Admonitions."

Houghton Mifflin Company for "The Wagon in the Barn," by John Drinkwater, from *All about Me,* and "Night Clouds," by Amy Lowell, from *What's O'Clock*. Each of these selections is used by permission of, and by arrangement with, Houghton Mifflin Company, the authorized publishers.

The Incorporated Society of Authors, Playwrights and Composers for "Mice," by Rose Fyleman, reprinted from *Fifty-One New Nursery Rhymes* (Methuen and Company) by permission of Miss Rose Fyleman.

Alfred A. Knopf, Inc., for "African Dance," by Langston Hughes, reprinted from *The Dream*

*Keeper;* "Little Brother's Secret," by Katharine Mansfield, reprinted from *Poems;* and "Madman's Song," by Elinor Wylie, reprinted from *Collected Poems.* Each of these selections is used by permission of and special arrangement with Alfred A. Knopf, Inc., authorized publishers.

Richard Le Gallienne for his "A Caravan from China Comes."

David Lloyd for "The Mirror," from the *Poems* of W. H. Davies (1934), by permission of Jonathan Cape, Ltd.

Macmillan and Company, Ltd., for "The Snare," by James Stephens, from *Collected Poems.*

The Macmillan Company for "Fairies" and "My Dog," by Marchette Gaylord Chute, from *Rhymes about Ourselves;* "The Milkman," by Leonard J. Feeney, from *Riddle and Reverie;* "The Snare," by James Stephens, from *Collected Poems;* and "The Falling Star," "February Twilight," and "Night," by Sara Teasdale, from *Stars To-night.*

The Medici Society for "Everybody Says," by Dorothy Aldis, from *Everything and Anything.*

*Modern Woman* for "Who's In?" by Elizabeth Fleming.

Thomas Bird Mosher for "From the Hills of Dream," "Hushing Song," and "The Valley of White Poppies," by Fiona Macleod.

John Murray for "Shops," by Winifred M. Letts.
Edward J. O'Brien for his "Irish."

The Paebar Company, Inc., for "Changeling" and "Wait's Carol," by Barbara Young.

Eric S. Pinker and Adrienne Morrison Incorporated, agents for the Mansfield Estate, for "Little Brother's Secret," by Katharine Mansfield.

James B. Pinker and Son for "Goldenhair," by James Joyce, from *Collected Poems,* published by Jonathan Cape, Ltd.

G. P. Putnam's Sons for "About Buttons," from *Here, There, and Everywhere,* and "Everybody Says," from *Everything and Anything,* by Dorothy Aldis.

Lexie Dean Robertson for her "Gossip."

Jessie B. Rittenhouse Scollard for "Out in the Wood," by Clinton Scollard.

Thomas Seltzer, Inc., for "Traveling Storm," by Mark Van Doren, from *Spring Thunder and Other Poems.*

Selwyn and Blount, Ltd., for "Hush Song," by Elizabeth Shane, from *By Bog and Sea in Donegal.*

R. Farquharson Sharp for "From the Hills of Dream," "Hushing Song," and "The Valley of White Poppies," by Fiona Macleod.

Simon and Schuster, Inc., for "The Lightship," by Josephine Johnson, from *Year's End.*

Cornelia Otis Skinner for her "The Path to Shottery."

Eleanor Slater for her "Misdirection," from *Quest*.

Frederick A. Stokes Company for "Welcome to the New Year," by Eleanor Farjeon, reprinted by permission from *Come Christmas*, copyright, 1927, by Frederick A. Stokes Company, and "I Heard It in the Valley," "I Keep Three Wishes Ready," and "I'm Wishing the Whole World Christmas," by Annette Wynne, reprinted by permission from *For Days and Days: A Year-round Treasury of Verse for Children*, copyright, 1919, by Frederick A. Stokes Company.

*Theatre Arts Monthly* for "The Path to Shottery," by Cornelia Otis Skinner.

Charles Hanson Towne for "I Heard a Bird Sing," by Oliver Herford.

Nancy Byrd Turner for her "Courage Has a Crimson Coat."

Mark Van Doren for his "Traveling Storm," from *Spring Thunder and Other Poems*.

The Viking Press, Inc., for "Goldenhair," by James Joyce, from *Collected Poems*, copyright, 1918, published by The Viking Press, Inc., New York.

Willett, Clark and Company for "Proof" and "Wind Is a Cat," by Ethel Romig Fuller, from *White Peaks and Green*.

Yale University Press for "Misdirection," by Eleanor Slater, from *Quest*.